Covert-Ops: The Legacy Characters & Locations

Stephen Barker

Published by Stephen Barker, 2024.

COVERT-OPS: THE LEGACY CHARACTERS & LOCATIONS

First edition. May 13, 2024.

Copyright © 2024 Stephen Barker.

ISBN: 979-8224435296

Written by Stephen Barker.

Covert-Ops: The Legacy Characters, Locations & Transport

Covert-Ops: By Stephen

Introduction

Welcome to the thrilling supplement to the acclaimed "Covert-Ops: The Legacy," where the cloak-and-dagger world of espionage awaits. Delve deeper into the heart-pounding saga with this essential companion, offering tantalising backstories, immersive locales, and a glimpse into the transport utilised by our intrepid team of operatives.

In the shadows of secrecy, the fate of nations hangs in the balance as Steve, the seasoned team leader, guides his elite unit through the perilous landscape of global intrigue. Joining him are Simon, the transport specialist with nerves of steel, and George, the deadly sniper whose precision knows no bounds.

Venture further into the ranks to uncover the enigmatic Derek, whose mastery of communications is matched only by his unwavering loyalty, and Lucy, the team's interrogator and sniper, whose past holds the key to unlocking the truth behind their mission.

The story takes place in various locations, such as the United Kingdom, Bonaire and St Kitts. Our heroes are in a race against time to stop a sinister plot that could disrupt the balance of power. However, as they deal with deception and betrayal, they soon realise that the greatest threats might come from within their own team.

Transportation is not just a means to an end—it's a lifeline in a world where every second counts. Whether they're traversing rugged SUV vehicles, soaring through the skies or boarding boats, every mode of transport is a vital tool in their arsenal, propelling them ever closer to their elusive target.

"Covert-Ops: The Legacy Supplement" is essential reading for fans of high-stakes action and heart-stopping suspense.

Click Below to purchase Covert-Ops: The Legacy and the rest of the series.

https://www.amazon.co.uk/gp/product/B08P4YN5CZ

Team Members

Character Description: Steve Barker

Name: Steve Barker:
> Nationality: English
> Age: 57
> Height: 5 feet 7 inches
> Build: Muscular
> Eyes: Captivating Blue
> Residence: Isle of Wight / England

Backstory

Steve Barker's story unfolded against the backdrop of Farnham, Hampshire, a quaint town where tales of bravery and honour echoed through the generations. Born and bred in this English idyll, Steve's journey into the world of military service began at the tender age of sixteen when he enlisted in the Royal Green Jackets. His decision was not a whim but a calling, an echo of the courage instilled in him by his father, a veteran of the British Navy.

Standing at 5 feet 7 inches, Steve bore a muscular build sculpted by the disciplined lifestyle of a military man. His captivating blue eyes, often described as piercing, were windows to a depth of experience and resilience that only a life of service could carve. Every inch of his physique told a story—a narrative of dedication, training, and commitment to a cause greater than himself.

Deployed to global conflict zones, Steve found himself in the heart of covert operations that demanded utmost secrecy and precision. His early years in the Royal Green Jackets became a crucible for his skills, and he quickly rose to prominence, showcasing not only exceptional planning abilities but also an uncanny expertise in explosives. Steve's talents weren't confined to executing missions; they extended to the meticulous analysis of complex situations.

The undercover operations were Steve's proving grounds. He became a master strategist, developing plans tailored to each mission's nuances. His meticulous approach and the flawless execution of plans became a hallmark of his style. His ability to adapt to changing circumstances, anticipate unforeseen challenges, and navigate the intricate dance of a covert operative's life set him apart.

As the years unfolded, Steve Barker evolved into an exceptional leader. His tactical skills were complemented by an innate ability to foster camaraderie within his team. Leading a group of veterans, Steve became the voice of reason in the chaos, the anchor that his comrades relied on during moments of uncertainty. His empathetic nature, combined with an unwavering determination, inspired others to push beyond their limits.

In the field, Steve's leadership saved lives and left an indelible impact on communities affected by conflicts. His legacy wasn't just a trail of successful missions; it was a testament to the power of teamwork, resilience, and unwavering commitment to a mission's objectives. His team respected and admired him, acknowledging his leadership qualities as the glue that held them together in the most challenging situations.

Despite his numerous accomplishments, Steve Barker remained grounded and humble. He recognised the power of continuous improvement and sought to enhance not only his skills but also those of his team. His belief in the collective strength of a well-coordinated unit underscored his leadership philosophy. This philosophy went beyond the battlefield, impacting the lives of those he served with and the communities touched by his missions.

In conclusion, Steve Barker was more than just a British Military Veteran; he was a living embodiment of dedication, adaptability, and leadership. Born in Farnham, Hampshire, his journey from the idyllic English town to the global theatre of conflict was marked by exceptional physical attributes, captivating blue eyes, and a muscular build. His expertise in planning and explosives and unwavering dedication to the mission solidified his reputation as an expert in his field. As the leader of a team of veterans, Steve Barker's legacy was not just a testament to individual prowess but a celebration of the power of teamwork and the enduring impact one man can have on the lives of many.

Character Profile: Lucy Hatton

Name: Lucy Hatton
    Nationality: English
    Age: 55
    Height: 5 feet 7 inches
    Eyes: Blue
    Residence: Isle of Wight / England

Backstory

Lucy Hatton, a resilient and determined English Military Veteran, stands at 5 feet 7 inches with a slim build. Her striking presence belies the countless untold stories held within her captivating blue eyes. Born in the historic city of Portsmouth, Hampshire, Lucy's journey unfolds as a testament to her dedication to physical fitness and rigorous military training.

Her military career traversed the demanding and secretive realm of the Intelligence Corps, where Lucy honed a vast array of specialised skills, setting her apart as a true force to be reckoned with. Her expertise in undercover operations allowed her to seamlessly adopt new personas, effectively gathering critical information and countering threats.

However, Lucy's path was not without its darker chapters. In a period of struggle, she found herself working as a mercenary for drug cartels. Now a regrettable part of her past, this phase served as a crucible, testing her mettle and acting as a catalyst for personal growth and transformation.

The realisation of the darkness pervading humanity dawned upon Lucy during her time as a mercenary. Witnessing the consequences of her actions firsthand, she made a conscious decision to redirect her life towards redemption. Determined to atone for her past and contribute to a just cause, Lucy sought a new purpose by joining forces with her current team.

Lucy's proficiency in the art of interrogation became a defining aspect of her character. Her uncanny ability to extract valuable information, regardless of an individual's resolve or resistance, showcased her psychological finesse and deep understanding of human behaviour. These skills became instrumental in subtly exploiting vulnerabilities and garnering critical insights that significantly contributed to her team's operations.

Her training as a sniper added another layer to Lucy's capabilities. Exceptional precision and an unyielding focus became synonymous with her character, enabling her to eliminate threats from a distance, safeguard her team, and achieve mission objectives with remarkable accuracy.

The formidable veteran Lucy has become today is a product of facing numerous challenges in combat and personally. While physical wounds may heal, it's the mental and emotional scars that have left a lasting impact. Lucy's ongoing struggle to overcome trauma and cultivate resilience highlights her unwavering determination and drive.

Her commitment to her teammates and the cause she now fights for has manifested in numerous vital accomplishments. Lucy's ability to adapt and thrive in the face of adversity is a testament to her skills and unwavering commitment. Despite her troubled past, she stands as a true hero, rising from the depths of darkness to become a beacon of hope and justice.

Lucy Hatton's intense dedication, unwavering resolve, and exceptional skills make her an invaluable asset to her team, country, and the fight against global threats. With each mission, she continues to grow, evolve, and redefine what being a resilient and formidable military veteran means.

As Lucy joins the team alongside Steve, George, Derek, and Simon after the mission on the Isle of Wight, her presence adds a layer of expertise and experience that complements the diverse skills of her comrades. Together, they form a cohesive unit, each member bringing their unique strengths to the forefront, united in their mission to protect and serve. Lucy Hatton's journey from darkness to redemption is a testament to the transformative power of resilience, commitment, and the unwavering pursuit of a noble cause.

Character Profile: Derek Barker

Name: Derek Barker
 Nationality: English
 Age: 57
 Height: 5 feet 9 inches
 Build: Muscular
 Eyes: Green
 Residence: St Bethanie

Backstory

Derek Barker, a distinguished English Military Veteran, stands at 5 feet 9 inches with a muscular build and captivating brown eyes. Born and raised in Southampton, England, Derek's journey into the military began in a working-class family that instilled a profound sense of duty and loyalty. His father, a former member of the Merchant Navy, sowed the seeds of respect for the military and a commitment to serving his country. Derek's early fascination with radios and electronics paved the way for a remarkable career as a communication technology expert.

Joining the Royal Green Jackets at 18, Derek quickly revealed his immense talent and dedication to his craft. His natural aptitude for communication technology, whether it be repairing radios, deciphering codes, or setting up communication networks, became evident. Derek underwent specialised training as a radio and communications expert, honing his skills in the field's technical and tactical aspects.

Deployed to various war zones worldwide, Derek played a pivotal role in ensuring seamless communication between different units and coordinating operations. His extensive knowledge of frequencies, encryption methods, and signal transmission allowed him to navigate even the most challenging and hostile environments. The specifics of Derek's achievements remain classified due to national security reasons, but his commendations, including a mention in dispatches, testify to his exceptional service.

Derek's unparalleled knowledge and technical expertise made him highly sought-after within the military. Commanding officers recognised and valued his skills, often requesting his presence for critical operations. As the team communications expert, Derek's responsibilities extended beyond repairing and operating radios. He played a crucial role in implementing encryption measures, detecting and countering enemy jamming attempts, and guiding other team members on proper radio protocols.

Standing at an impressive 6 feet tall, Derek possessed a strong and lean build acquired through years of military training. His short, sandy-blond beard accentuated his well-defined jawline, while his piercing blue eyes exuded determination and intelligence. Despite the ruggedness associated with military life, Derek's friendly smile put those around him at ease.

Derek's stoic and disciplined personality traits, shaped by his military upbringing and training, made him exceptional at his job. His unwavering focus, attention to detail, and strong sense of duty meant he was always willing to go above and beyond to accomplish the mission and protect his comrades.

His greatest strength lies in his technical expertise in communication technology. An encyclopaedic knowledge of radio equipment, encryption methods, and signal transmission enabled Derek to troubleshoot and resolve issues efficiently. He was also an excellent problem solver, capable of thinking quickly on his feet and adapting to rapidly changing situations.

However, Derek's intense focus on his work occasionally led to a tendency to neglect personal relationships or self-care. His relentless pursuit of excellence sometimes bordered on perfectionism, causing him to be overly critical of himself and others. Despite these weaknesses, Derek's quirks and habits, such as always carrying a small notepad and a pen, showcased his exceptional organisational skills and dedication to his craft.

In conclusion, Derek Barker emerged as a highly skilled and dedicated military veteran who played a vital role as a radio and communications expert. His upbringing in Southampton, England, coupled with his natural abilities and unwavering commitment to duty, shaped him into a highly respected and indispensable member of the Royal Green Jackets. As Derek becomes a member of the team alongside Steve, George, and Simon after the mission on St Halb, his expertise and unique skills add a crucial layer to the team's capabilities, forging a bond that goes beyond professional duty.

Character Profile: George James

Name: George James
   Nationality: English
   Age: 47
   Height: 5 feet 9 inches
   Build: Muscular
   Eyes: Brown
   Residence: Birmingham / England

Backstory

George James, a resilient and seasoned English Military Veteran, stands at 5 feet 9 inches with a muscular build and captivating brown eyes that reflect his determination and sense of purpose. Born into a working-class family in Birmingham, England, George's childhood was shaped by financial hardships that instilled in him the values of hard work, determination, and loyalty. These foundational principles would become the cornerstone of his character and military career.

Education played a pivotal role in George's journey. Attending a local public school, he excelled academically while developing a strong interest in physical fitness and the military. At 18, driven by a deep-seated desire to serve his country and explore his innate talents, George deliberately chose to enlist in the British Army, setting the stage for a remarkable military career.

George's journey unfolded within the prestigious Grenadier Guards, where his dedication, discipline, and passion quickly propelled him through the ranks, earning him the respect and admiration of his comrades. His exceptional marksmanship skills caught the attention of superiors, leading to specialised training as a sniper. George's focus, precision, and ability to remain calm under pressure made him a valuable asset to his unit.

The crucible of war zones across the globe became George's testing ground. Deployed to highly volatile regions like Afghanistan and Iraq, he faced countless life-or-death situations, putting his training and skills to the ultimate test. His adaptability, split-second decision-making, and unwavering commitment to prioritising the safety of his team earned him a reputation as a capable and trusted leader.

During his first deployment, George found himself in a vulnerable position in Afghanistan's unforgiving terrain when his unit was ambushed. Despite being outnumbered and under heavy fire, his keen situational awareness allowed him to identify the enemy's positions. George, displaying exceptional courage, successfully eliminated several threats and held off the attack long enough for reinforcements to arrive.

The theatres of war expanded to Iraq, where George's leadership skills shone brightly. Taking charge of a high-stakes operation to rescue a captured intelligence officer, he demonstrated meticulous planning and led his team through hostile territory. The enemy was neutralised, and the mission concluded with the safe return of their comrade. These anecdotes etched George's name in the annals of military valour.

Personality-wise, George James is distinguished by his unwavering loyalty, composure, and selflessness. A natural leader, he leads by example, consistently placing the needs of his team and country above his own. Despite the hardships faced in war zones, George maintains an optimistic outlook and a solid moral compass. His charismatic nature and the ability to build strong bonds make him a respected figure amongst colleagues, serving as a source of inspiration for younger soldiers.

George is formidable physically, with his muscular build and height of 5 feet 9 inches. His captivating brown eyes reflect determination and embody the depth of experiences witnessed in the crucible of conflict.

In conclusion, George James emerged as a seasoned military veteran with a distinction earned in the renowned Grenadier Guards. Shaped by his upbringing, personality traits, and unwavering dedication to serving his country, he embodies the true spirit of a soldier. The record of bravery, leadership, and resilience paints a portrait of George as a guardian dedicated to protecting his country and comrades. As he embarks on a new chapter alongside Steve, Simon, and the team, George's rich history becomes a testament to the indomitable spirit of those who answer the call of duty.

Character Profile: Simon Munnery

Name: Simon Munnery
  Nationality: English
  Age: 57
  Height: 6 feet 2 inches
  Build: Slim
  Eyes: Green
  Residence: Barnstable / England

Backstory

Simon Munnery, a distinguished British Military Veteran from the serene town of Barnstaple in Devon, England, stands tall at 6 feet 2 inches with a slim physique and captivating green eyes. Growing up in a close-knit community, Simon's patriotic upbringing instilled a profound sense of duty and gratitude toward his country. Fuelled by a desire to serve and protect, Simon made the life-altering decision to enlist in the army at 18.

His career unfolded as a tank commander in the Queens Royal Hussars, marked by moments of brilliance and commendation. Deployed in various conflicts worldwide, notably in Iraq and Afghanistan, Simon emerged as a reliable and knowledgeable expert in all aspects of mechanical engineering.

Simon's exceptional skills in mechanical engineering have made him an indispensable asset to the team. Serving as the team's esteemed transport expert, he ensures the seamless functioning of all vehicles, providing vital support for successful mission execution. Simon's extensive knowledge and expertise enable him to quickly diagnose and resolve mechanical issues, safeguarding the team's safety and preventing obstacles that might impede progress.

One noteworthy instance illustrating Simon's resourcefulness occurred during a harrowing mission in Afghanistan. Faced with severe damage to the team's primary transport vehicle due to an IED explosion, Simon transformed into an engineering genius. Utilising spare parts salvaged from nearby vehicles and applying his creative mind, he jury-rigged a temporary solution, allowing the team to evacuate and receive necessary medical attention safely.

Simon's commitment to the mission and his comrades is a hallmark of his character. His disciplined work ethic inspires others, and his ability to remain calm under pressure is instrumental in finding practical solutions to mitigate risks and ensure the team's success. Known for going above and beyond the call of duty, Simon consistently demonstrates his passion for his vocation and unwavering commitment to his comrades.

Simon's personality is characterised by poise and high discipline. Despite his impressive skills and achievements, he remains humble and approachable, always willing to share his knowledge with others. His calm and composed demeanour allows him to make level-headed decisions even in high-stress situations. Beyond his military responsibilities, Simon actively seeks opportunities to mentor younger team members, fostering their growth and development.

In conclusion, Simon Munnery is a British Military Veteran whose exemplary career, exceptional skills in mechanical engineering, and unwavering dedication make him a precious member of any team. With a deep sense of patriotism, strong problem-solving abilities, and a natural inclination to lead, Simon continues to inspire those around him with his passion for service and relentless pursuit of excellence. As he becomes a team member alongside Steve and George, Simon's unique skills and experiences further enrich the team's capabilities, creating a cohesive and formidable unit ready to face any challenge.

The Legacy Characters

Character Profile: Hadley Barker

Name: Hadley Barker
   Nationality: English
   Age: 16
   Height: 5 feet 8 inches
   Occupation: Carpenter
   Eyes: Green
   Residence: England

Backstory

Hadley Barker's story begins in the maritime city of Southampton, where he was born and raised. Hadley, the only son of Steve Barker, a former special forces veteran, had a childhood steeped in an environment that emphasised discipline, resilience, and self-reliance. Though frequently away on missions, his father made a conscious effort to instil in Hadley the importance of family, leaving an indelible mark on the young boy.

From the tender age of 8, Hadley found solace and inspiration in the basement workshop his father had set up. Steve, recognising his son's budding interest, became Hadley's first mentor in carpentry. Under his father's guidance, Hadley developed a keen eye for detail and a passion for crafting things with his hands. Carpentry became not just a skill for him but an outlet for creativity and a medium to express himself.

Simultaneously, Hadley's adventurous spirit led him to discover a local taekwondo academy. Drawn to the martial art's discipline, power, and grace, he enrolled in classes with his father's and mother's encouragement. Hadley's dedication to taekwondo soon became evident, and he progressed rapidly, eventually assuming the role of a trainer in the academy, sharing his knowledge and becoming a mentor to fellow students.

STEPHEN BARKER

Significant milestones marked Hadley's life as a carpenter and taekwondo practitioner. At the age of 13, he clinched first place in a regional carpentry competition, earning recognition for his exceptional craftsmanship. This victory bolstered his confidence and fuelled his determination to excel in carpentry and martial arts.

However, Hadley faced his greatest challenge when his father was injured during a mission, rendering him unable to return home. Suddenly, the young teenager found himself thrust into a world without the guidance of his role model. This period tested Hadley's resilience but became a crucible that strengthened his character. Taking on additional responsibilities, such as managing the family's finances and caring for his mother, Hadley remained determined to succeed.

Steve's military background played a pivotal role in shaping Hadley's character. The stories of sacrifice, duty, and honour became a part of Hadley's identity, instilling in him a profound respect for these values. He internalised the importance of dedication and determination, striving to emulate these qualities in his own life.

Motivated by a desire to honour his father's legacy while forging his path, Hadley aspires to become a renowned carpenter, participating in national competitions to showcase his talent. In taekwondo, he dreams of earning his black belt and representing his country in international tournaments. Beyond personal achievements, Hadley seeks to inspire others, illustrating that with hard work and passion, anyone can achieve greatness.

Hadley Barker emerges as a captivating protagonist; his resilience, determination, and multifaceted capabilities make him a compelling character. His backstory, coupled with mastery in carpentry and taekwondo and the influence of his father's military background, positions him as a character with immense depth and potential for growth throughout the narrative. As his story unfolds, the kidnapping of his sisters becomes a turning point that propels him into a new chapter, drawing him into a team alongside Steve, George, Derek, and

Simon, where his unique skills and experiences add a new layer to the group dynamic.

Character Profile: Bethanie Barker

Name: Bethanie Barker
 Nationality: English
 Age: 31
 Height: 5 feet 5 inches
 Occupation: Lawyer, Caregiver
 Residence: Totton / England
 Eyes: Blue

Backstory

Bethanie Barker's narrative unfolds in the quaint town where her father, a former special forces veteran, raised her. His military background significantly shaped Bethanie's childhood, infusing it with lessons of survival, toughness, and resilience. As a witness to her father's sacrifices for their family, Bethanie developed a profound appreciation for commitment and protection, which would become central to her character.

Determined to make her mark in a challenging profession, Bethanie pursued a career in law. She earned a scholarship to a prestigious law school, excelling academically, demonstrating her intellectual prowess and commitment to her ambitions. Balancing her studies, Bethanie took on part-time jobs to support both herself and her father, embodying the resilience instilled in her by his military teachings.

After graduating at the top of her class, Bethanie secured a coveted position at a prominent law firm in the city. Her sharp intellect, persuasive advocacy skills, and unwavering commitment to justice quickly set her apart in the legal arena. Despite the demanding nature of her career, Bethanie's journey wasn't confined to the courtroom.

In a parallel role that defined her life, Bethanie took on the responsibility of caring for her disabled son, Joshua. This role, requiring round-the-clock attention, tested Bethanie's resilience and love. Her commitment to Joshua became a driving force, inspiring her to provide the best life possible for her son.

Juggling the demands of a high-stakes legal career and caregiving responsibilities, Bethanie faced numerous challenges. The balancing act between work and her son's needs often led to sacrifices of personal time and social activities. Bethanie's life became a testament to her conviction that professional success and dedication to family were not mutually exclusive.

As a caregiver, Bethanie confronted scepticism and judgment from colleagues. However, her determination and unyielding belief in her priorities fuelled her ability to push through societal expectations. Her resilience shone through in the face of obstacles, embodying the mental fortitude she acquired through her father's military influence.

The challenges Bethanie encountered in her journey were further compounded by the complexities of raising a disabled child. Her advocacy for Joshua's needs demonstrated her fearlessness in navigating the intricacies of the healthcare system. Bethanie's ceaseless efforts involved researching the latest medical advancements and connecting with support groups to ensure her son received optimal care.

Her narrative culminates in a character embodying fearlessness, determination, and unwavering dedication to career and family. Bethanie's strength lies in navigating life's complexities and maintaining her sense of self and purpose. As her story progresses, the kidnapping of Bethanie by Alex Acosta's drug cartel becomes a pivotal turning point, propelling her into a realm where her resilience and resourcefulness are tested to their limits.

Character Profile: Abbie Barker

Name: Abbie Barker
   Nationality: English
   Age: 32
   Height: 5 feet 5 inches
   Occupation: Care worker
   Eyes: Green
   Residence: Totton / England

Backstory

Abbie Barker's story begins in the small town of Totton, where her father, a former special forces veteran, raised her. The lessons of resilience and strength instilled in her from a young age shaped Abbie's character, setting the foundation for a life dedicated to caring for others.

Growing up in Totton, Abbie attended local schools where her natural aptitude for empathy and understanding became evident. She developed a keen interest in the healthcare industry as she progressed through her education. After high school, she decided to pursue a nursing career, enrolling in a nursing program to turn her passion for caring into a profession.

During her training, Abbie faced the challenges inherent in healthcare. She encountered patients dealing with debilitating illnesses, witnessing their pain and despair. Despite these problematic situations, Abbie persevered, providing comfort and support to those in need. These early experiences deepened her understanding of the profound impact she could have on others and solidified her determination to make a positive difference in people's lives.

Her father's influence was crucial to her personal and professional development. He shared his war stories, offering Abbie a unique perspective of resilience, adaptability, and selflessness. Abbie internalised these lessons, carrying them with her into her career as a care worker.

Throughout her career, Abbie faced numerous obstacles and setbacks, each contributing to her personal growth. The challenges she encountered fuelled her determination, teaching her that even in moments of pain and exhaustion, she could find the strength to persevere. Abbie's resilience became a personal asset and an inspiration to those around her, creating a culture of determination in her workplace.

Abbie's dedication and empathetic approach to caregiving elevated her standing in Totton's healthcare community. She became a highly regarded care worker, known for her commitment to her patients and her continuous pursuit of professional development. Workshops and training sessions became a regular part of Abbie's routine as she sought to expand her skill set and stay updated on the latest techniques and therapies.

In her professional life, Abbie built solid and meaningful relationships with her patients. Taking the time to understand their needs and feelings, she went above and beyond to ensure they received the best care possible. Abbie's empathy and profound connection with others earned her patients' and their families' trust and respect.

In conclusion, Abbie Barker's journey is one of strength, resilience, and compassion. Her upbringing, education, and early experiences shaped her into a compassionate and tenacious care worker. Abbie's dedication to her work, personal growth, and professional achievements have made her a pillar in the healthcare industry. By providing compassionate care and support, Abbie continues to make a positive and lasting impact on the lives of those she cares for in the tight-knit community of Totton.

Character Description: Alex Acosta, Leader of a Drug Cartel

Name: Alex Acosta
  Nationality: Spanish
  Age: 45
  Height: 5 feet 7 inches
  Build: Muscular
  Eyes: brown
  Residence: St Kitts

Backstory

Alex Acosta, a shadowy figure with an insatiable appetite for power and revenge, emerged from the turbulent underbelly of a sprawling metropolis. From the chaos and violence of his childhood, he crafted an empire of blood and fear, inheriting the legacy of his infamous uncle, Henry.

Born into a world marred by addiction and neglect, Alex's parents abandoned him to the merciless streets. It was amid the rundown tenements and vice-ridden alleys that he learned life's cruellest lessons. Instead of succumbing to the harsh realities, Alex's keen mind absorbed knowledge like a sponge. This intelligence and ruthless determination propelled him through his uncle's drug cartel ranks.

His ascent was marked by calculated moves, outsmarting and eliminating rivals with a cold precision that bordered on brilliance. Respect and fear followed him, solidifying his position as the undisputed leader. But beneath the pursuit of power lay a deeper motive – an unquenchable thirst for retribution against those who had wronged him.

Alex's first targets were his parents, who blamed him for his wretched upbringing. Their orchestrated deaths were chilling manifestations of his depravity. His lethal tactics were a testament to his cunning intellect as he navigated the dangerous world of cartels. Every move and decision was crafted meticulously, ensuring his empire remained unchallenged.

His enigmatic personality served as a shield, a charm that endeared him to subordinates and commanded their unwavering loyalty. Yet, a complex, tormented soul lurked behind the facade. The loss of his uncle, a mentor and the closest thing to family, scarred him deeply. His relentless pursuit of power became a personal vendetta to protect Henry's legacy.

Despite his imposing exterior, Alex grappled with inner demons. A haunting loss drove his ruthless determination to preserve his power. The void left by his uncle's death fuelled a desire for vengeance, a hunger for retribution against those who dared to challenge the legacy of Henry Acosta.

His piercing and authoritative gaze induced fear in allies and enemies alike. Rumours of his physical prowess and mercilessness circulated like whispers in the underworld. Hand-to-hand combat and mastery of weapons transformed Alex into a formidable threat, a force that operated in the dark recesses of crime and power.

As he thrived in the murky realm of cartels, questions lingered about the ember of humanity buried within him. Would it fuel his ultimate downfall, or could it be the spark of redemption? Alex Acosta's existence, defined by shadows and stained by vengeance, remained a mystery shrouded in the darkness he had crafted for himself.

The web of power and revenge he wove led him to a fateful decision – the kidnapping of Steve Barker's daughters. In a macabre act of vengeance, he sought to make those responsible for his uncle's death suffer as he had suffered. The story of Alex Acosta, a man whose name struck fear into hearts, unfolded against the backdrop of the grim underworld he ruled. In this world, power, vengeance, and the remnants of humanity collided in a dangerous dance.

Nico Martinez – Alex's right-hand man.

Name: Nico Martinez
  Nationality: Spanish
  Age: 40
  Height: 5 feet 7 inches
  Build: Muscular
  Eyes: Captivating brown
  Residence: St Kitts

Backstory

Nicholas "Nico" Martinez, a towering figure with a captivating intensity, stands as the loyal right-hand man and confidant of Alex Acosta, the enigmatic leader of a notorious drug cartel. At 40, Nico's life journey has woven a complex tapestry of charisma, ambition, and a calculating nature within the seedy underbelly of Mexico City.

Raised in poverty, Nico swiftly learned the harsh realities of his environment, understanding that power held the key to transcending his circumstances. This understanding led him to align himself with those in control, ultimately crossing paths with Alex. Recognising Nico's potential, Alex took him under his wing, providing mentorship that shaped Nico into the fiercely loyal lieutenant he is today.

Physically imposing at 6'2" with a muscular build, Nico's Mexican heritage is evident in his olive skin and sharp, angular features. His dark, penetrating eyes reflect an unwavering loyalty to Alex and the cartel's cause. While Alex exudes magnetic charm, Nico maintains a more severe and reserved demeanour, perpetually aware of the dangers lurking in the shadows.

Nico's role within the cartel goes beyond mere muscle; he orchestrates day-to-day operations. His keen eye for detail and sharp analytical skills grant him a profound understanding of the cartel's intricacies. From ensuring the seamless flow of drugs across borders to managing a vast network of informants and enforcers, Nico's unwavering dedication and systematic approach are integral to the cartel's dominance.

Operating in stark contrast to Alex's flamboyant nature, Nico masters discretion and subtlety. He works behind the scenes, using influence and connections to manipulate rivals and strengthen the cartel's position. His calculated diplomacy and ability to predict adversaries' moves make him a formidable opponent. While intensely loyal, Nico grapples with internal conflicts, questioning the moral implications of his actions and confronting the humanity buried beneath his scarred soul.

Nico's interactions with cartel members are delicate, balancing authority and respect while remaining vigilant for potential betrayals. His loyalty to Alex inspires both admiration and fear among members, showcasing the lengths he would go to protect their leader and the cartel's legacy. The symbiotic relationship between Nico and Alex elevates the cartel's influence, reaching unimaginable heights through their combined ruthlessness and cunning.

Despite his loyalty, Nico's vulnerabilities become apparent as the story unfolds. Internal conflicts push him to question his loyalties and the cost of his actions. His journey tests the limits of his allegiance to Alex, forcing decisions that could reshape the cartel's landscape. Torn between the morality he struggles to hold onto and the darkness he has embraced, Nico's character evolves, adding depth and complexity to the narrative.

As the intricate dynamics of the drug cartel unravel, Nico's internal struggles become a focal point. The story explores the price of power, the morality within the shadows, and the profound impact of choices made in pursuit of dominance. In Nicholas "Nico" Martinez, the narrative finds a character whose complexities contribute to the unfolding drama, bringing depth to the world of crime and power.

Lucas Aakster

Name: Lucas
   Nationality: Dutch
   Age: 37
   Height: 5 feet 7 inches
   Build: skinny
   Eyes: brown
   Residence: Bonaire

Backstory

Lucas Aakster, the enigmatic and morally ambiguous figure from the island of Bonaire, presents a facade of unassuming normalcy that conceals the complexities within. Standing at a modest 5 feet 7 inches with a slender build, Lucas's unremarkable appearance masks the strength and cunning that define him. At 37, he carries the weight of a turbulent and complicated life, veiled behind a stoic expression that rarely reveals his genuine emotions.

Lucas's almond-shaped hazel eyes, set beneath sharp, arched eyebrows, betray hints of intelligence and weariness. These windows to his conflicted soul reflect the inner struggles and moral dilemmas that plague him. His jet-black hair, neatly trimmed and slicked back, symbolises his calculated and deliberate nature, every strand reflecting the meticulous and precise personality that lies beneath the surface.

Despite his composed exterior, Lucas's mannerisms betray the torment within. Fidgeting with his cufflinks, a nervous tic exposes his inner turmoil and the weight of his involvement with the notorious drug cartel led by Alex Acosta. His upbringing in the heart of the island, surrounded by poverty and violence, laid the foundation for his entanglement in a world of organised crime.

Lucas's parents struggled to provide basic necessities, and the allure of power and wealth associated with the drug cartel became a tempting escape from a life of destitution. Drawn into their operations, his involvement escalated from petty theft to more dangerous roles. Yet, each choice he made carried consequences that rippled through his own life and those around him.

As Lucas navigated the complex world of organised crime, internal conflicts intensified. The choices driven by desperation clashed with the guilt gnawing at his conscience. Torn between the desire for a life of luxury and the remnants of empathy within him, Lucas found himself in a morally ambiguous existence. He grappled with the fragile boundary between the victim and the perpetrator, forced into the darkest corners of society by circumstances beyond his control.

In Lucas's story, readers are confronted with an intricate exploration of the human condition. The devastating effects of poverty and limited opportunities are laid bare, illustrating how individuals can be driven into the shadows of society. Simultaneously, the narrative prompts reflection on personal responsibility and individual choices, blurring the lines between right and wrong in a seldom black-and-white world.

As the tale unfolds, Lucas's character becomes a vessel for broader questions about morality, resilience, and the intricate dance between necessity and choice. His complexities draw readers into the shadows of the human experience, challenging preconceived notions and urging an exploration of the factors that shape individuals into the enigmatic figures they become.

Character Description: Carlos Abele

Name: Carlos Abele
   Nationality: Dutch
   Age: 68
   Height: 5 feet 8 inches
   Build: skinny
   Eyes: brown
   Residence: Bonaire

Backstory

Carlos Alebe, once a name echoing through the alleys of Bonaire as the proud owner of a modest shop, has seen the kaleidoscope of life's colours shift drastically. Like the waves caressing the island's shores, his journey has been tumultuous, marked by the brutal erosion of dreams and the silent agony of shattered aspirations.

Born into a humble family on the Dutch island of Bonaire, Carlos inherited the spirit of resilience that danced through the veins of his ancestors. As a young man, he harboured dreams of creating a space where locals and tourists alike could find a piece of Bonaire to call their own. Guided by this vision, Carlos invested his savings in opening a quaint shop nestled in a corner of the bustling marketplace.

For years, Carlos's shop was more than just a business; it was a sanctuary where the island's stories unfolded. Locals gathered to share laughter, and tourists discovered treasures that held the essence of Bonaire's rich culture. However, the idyllic narrative of Carlos's life took an unexpected turn when the looming shadow of Alex Acosta's drug cartel cast its malevolent gaze upon him.

The cartel, known for its ruthless tactics and insidious grip on the island's underbelly, demanded a protection fee from local businesses. Carlos, barely making ends meet, found himself trapped in the clutches of a coercive ultimatum. Unable to afford the protection money, he faced the grim reality of retribution.

When Carlos's modest store refused to yield to the cartel's demands, the response was swift and brutal. In the dead of night, flames engulfed the once-vibrant establishment, reducing it to smouldering ruins. The inferno not only devoured the physical remnants of Carlos's dreams but also left an indelible mark on his spirit.

With no insurance to rebuild and no savings left to revive his business, Carlos Alebe became a casualty of a power struggle that played out silently in the narrow streets of Bonaire. The man who once welcomed customers with a warm smile now roamed the very alleys that had witnessed the unravelling of his livelihood.

Homelessness became Carlos's unwelcome companion, and the streets of Bonaire became both his refuge and purgatory. Stripped of the title of a shop owner, he became an anonymous figure blending into the backdrop of the island's daily life. The once-proud entrepreneur navigated the challenges of living without shelter, scavenging for sustenance, and seeking solace in the remnants of his shattered dreams.

Amid the harsh realities of homelessness, Carlos's spirit remained unbroken. He refused to succumb to the bitterness that threatened to consume him. Instead, he became a silent observer of the island's rhythms, finding solace in the simple joys that the streets offered—a fleeting sunset, the laughter of children playing by the beach, and the warmth of shared stories among fellow souls battered by life's storms.

On one of these days, as he sheltered from the hot sun, Carlos Albee's path converged with an unexpected twist of fate. Huddled in the shadows of an old, ruined building, remnants of an era long past, he found himself witness to an unforeseen alliance—the arrival of a team brought together by a shared purpose.

Intrigued by the resilience etched into Carlos's features, Steve, the former special forces veteran leading the motley crew, approached the weathered man sitting in solitude. A conversation unfolded, and layers of Carlos's untold story began to unravel. The team, recognising a kindred spirit weathered by life's storms, invited Carlos to lead them to a house belonging to Lucas.

As reluctant embers of hope flickered within him, Carlos Alebe, the once proud shop owner turned homeless wanderer, found himself on the cusp of a new chapter. With the shadows of the past clinging to his every step, he embarked on a journey that held the promise of redemption—a chance to reclaim his dignity, stand against the forces that had robbed him of his dreams, and perhaps rebuild the sanctuary he had lost in the ashes of betrayal.

Character Description: Miguel Fernandes

Name: Miguel Fernandes
   Nationality: African
   Age: 50
   Height: 5 feet 8 inches
   Build: Stocky
   Eyes: Brown
   Residence: St Kitts

Backstory

Miguel Fernandes, a figure deeply ingrained in the essence of St. Kitts, emerged from the sun-drenched tapestry of Caribbean life. Born into the azure seas, golden sands, and vibrant colours that define the island, his roots anchored him to a life devoted to justice and community service. From a tender age, Miguel sensed the collective responsibility to nurture and protect his home—a sentiment instilled by the elders who painted tales of duty and guardianship.

Before he donned the uniform of the St. Kitts Police Force, Miguel's journey unfolded in a different realm—the disciplined world of the military. As a young man, he ventured into the elite echelons of the Special Forces, where he honed his skills and forged an unbreakable resolve. The uniform became a second skin, the emblem of a soldier who had weathered storms far beyond the tranquil shores of St. Kitts.

Miguel's journey into the Special Forces was a crucible that tempered his mettle. The trials of training, the camaraderie of his fellow soldiers, and the high-stakes missions etched the contours of his character. The experiences in the military became the crucible where Miguel's resilience and dedication were tested, preparing him for a life of service to come.

COVERT-OPS: THE LEGACY CHARACTERS & LOCATIONS

As a special forces soldier, Miguel traversed landscapes far removed from the serene beaches of St. Kitts. His missions were shadows in the night, covert operations that required precision and unwavering commitment. The skills acquired in those years would become the foundation upon which he'd later build his legacy as a guardian of the island.

At 5 feet 8 inches, Miguel's robust and stocky build reflects years of disciplined service and a commitment to physical fitness. The distinguished marks etched on his features bear witness to the wisdom acquired over five decades of island life. Dark, warm eyes mirror the depths of his dedication, gleaming with a quiet resolve—testimony to the storms weathered both in the military and law enforcement.

Clad in the uniform of the St. Kitts Police Force, Miguel carries himself with a blend of authority and approachability. His neatly maintained appearance, punctuated by the badge pinned to his chest, symbolises a duty interwoven with the very fabric of St. Kitts. The uniform isn't just clothing; it's a testament to his life's mission.

Miguel's transition from the military to law enforcement was seamless, a natural progression fuelled by an innate sense of duty. Returning to St. Kitts with a wealth of experience, he joined the ranks of the police force. The echoes of military precision and the bonds forged in the crucible of service became valuable assets in his new role.

Within the precinct, Miguel's leadership became defined by a quiet but commanding presence. Dedication to justice earned him a reputation as a stalwart defender of the island's peace. His experiences in the military remained the unspoken foundation, providing him with insights that transcended the routine of law enforcement.

In the present day, St. Kitts's tranquillity faces internal and external challenges. At 50 years old, Miguel Fernandes, a seasoned guardian, finds himself at the forefront of a battle against new shadows that threaten the island. His dedication to preserving the peace is unyielding, but the challenges become pivotal in a tale that tests the resilience of St. Kitts.

Within this backdrop, Miguel Fernandes encounters a force that transcends the boundaries of his familiar terrain—the arrival of a team led by the seasoned veteran Steve. Together, they stand on the precipice of unfolding events that will test the island's defences. The alliance becomes a beacon of hope, drawing upon Miguel's local knowledge and the team's expertise.

Miguel Fernandes emerges as more than a law enforcement officer. He becomes a guide, a source of wisdom, and a bridge between the team and the intricacies of St. Kitts. He is a character whose roots run deep, a guardian who, with weathered hands and a heart etched with the tales of his homeland, stands resolute in the face of adversity, ready to defend the island he calls home.

Character Description: Hugo Acosta

Name: Hugo Acosta
   Nationality: Spanish
   Age: 20
   Height: 6 feet 0 inches
   Build: Slim
   Eyes: Blue
   Residence: From St Kitts, now living in London

Backstory

Hugo Acosta's journey into the dark alleys of organised crime began when most teenagers were still navigating the complexities of adolescence. Born into the notorious Acosta legacy, his life was destined to take a perilous path from the moment he drew his first breath. Hugo, the eldest son of Alex Acosta, was groomed to inherit a kingdom of shadows, a realm built on power, wealth, and the illicit trade that flowed like poison through the veins of the underworld.

Growing up in the wealthy shadows cast by his father's empire, Hugo witnessed the inner workings of the drug cartel from an early age. The hushed conversations, the clandestine meetings, and the ever-present aura of danger painted a vivid backdrop to his childhood. While other kids played in parks, Hugo's playgrounds were the dimly lit corners of his family's mansion, where whispered secrets held more weight than any bedtime story.

By the tender age of 14, Hugo had graduated from the fabled school of organised crime. His initiation began with seemingly innocent tasks—transporting small quantities of drugs across the tranquil streets of St. Kitts. But innocence evaporated like morning dew as he embraced the dark allure of his family's legacy. The Caribbean winds that whispered through the palms carried the seeds of Hugo's transformation into a pawn in his father's treacherous game.

Hugo's ascent through the cartel's ranks was as swift as it was inevitable. The streets that once seemed mundane became a labyrinth of secrets, and he navigated them with the ease of a seasoned navigator. By 16, he had graduated from simple courier duties to overseeing distribution networks. The tendrils of his influence reached far and wide, ensnaring those who dared challenge the supremacy of the Acosta cartel.

His eyes, the colour of an ocean storm, reflected the tempest within—Blue, like the cold detachment that characterised his approach to business. With a slim build that belied the iron will beneath, Hugo became a living embodiment of the Acosta legacy—a legacy that demanded unwavering loyalty and exacted ruthless consequences.

At the cusp of adulthood, Hugo's realm expanded beyond the Caribbean shores. His father, recognising the need to secure the family's empire, entrusted him with a formidable task. At 20, Hugo Alcosta found himself at the helm of the international arm of the drug smuggling operation. London, a city steeped in history, became the stage for his sinister symphony.

The city's bustling streets and towering structures became the canvas for Hugo's ambitions. From the shadows, he orchestrated a complex dance of trafficking routes, money laundering, and strategic alliances. The London skyline, often cloaked in mist, mirrored the veiled operations under Hugo's command—imposing, formidable, and shrouded in secrecy.

His father's empire, once confined to the whispers of the Caribbean waves, now echoes through the cobblestone streets of London. Alex Acosta's legacy casts a long shadow, but Hugo moved within it, orchestrating a web of crime that spanned continents.

Yet, beneath the veneer of power, Hugo grappled with demons lurking in his conscience's recesses. The choices he made cast shadows upon his soul, like scars etched into the tapestry of his existence. The weight of his actions, the lives entangled in the web he wove, and the echoes of betrayal haunted his nights.

A man of contradictions, Hugo was torn between filial duty and a desire for something beyond the shadows of his family's legacy. He found solace in the high-rises of London, gazing over the city he now controlled. Yet, with each victory, an invisible chain tightened around his heart, tethering him to a destiny he never chose.

Hugo's operations unfolded in the city's heart amidst the looming skyscrapers that seemed to touch the heavens. His blue eyes, often windows to the storm within, caught glimpses of those who dared challenge the kingdom he sought to expand. Unbeknownst to him, Hugo Alcosta's destiny became intertwined with a force that transcended the boundaries of criminal enterprises.

Character Description: Joseph Belboda

Name: Joseph Belboda
    Nationality: Kittian
    Age: 26
    Height: 5 feet 7 inches
    Build: Slim
    Eyes: brown
    Residence: From St Kitts

Backstory

In the sun-soaked landscapes of St. Kitts, where the Caribbean waves caress the shores with rhythmic serenity, Joseph Belboda's story unfolded against the backdrop of a paradisiacal island tainted by the shadows of organised crime. Born into the embrace of azure seas and golden sands, Joseph's journey took an ominous turn when he became entangled in the web of the notorious Alex Acosta cartel.

Joseph's childhood, though kissed by the tropical sun, bore witness to the darker realities that lurked in the island's underbelly. Raised in modest circumstances, his family struggled to make ends meet, and the allure of the criminal underworld became increasingly difficult to resist. At the tender age of 16, when most youths were navigating the turbulence of adolescence, Joseph made a fateful decision that would reshape the trajectory of his life.

Drawn to the promises of wealth and power, Joseph joined the ranks of the Alex Acosta cartel. The clandestine meetings in dimly lit corners became his new reality, and the secrets whispered in hushed tones were his initiation into a world governed by rules that transcended legality. His slim build and unassuming demeanour masked an ambition that burned within—a hunger for recognition, influence, and a life beyond the constraints of his humble beginnings.

COVERT-OPS: THE LEGACY CHARACTERS & LOCATIONS

As a low-ranking member of the cartel, Joseph navigated the treacherous paths of drug trafficking with a blend of audacity and caution. He became a pawn in the grand chessboard of criminal enterprises, learning the rules of the game through first-hand experiences that left indelible marks on his journey.

Driven by an insatiable desire to rise above his station, Joseph took on increasingly risky assignments. Smuggling operations, discreet transactions, and alliances forged in the twilight of secrecy became his stepping stones. His willingness to take risks, coupled with a knack for navigating the volatile world of organised crime, garnered him attention from higher-ups in the cartel.

As Joseph moved deeper into the shadows, he discovered that the ascent through the ranks was not merely about cunning and resourcefulness—it demanded a compromise of one's principles and an unwavering loyalty to the Acosta legacy. The tendrils of the cartel's influence reached into every facet of his life, pulling him deeper into a realm where morality was a scarce commodity.

Now, at 26 years old, Joseph Belboda stands at a crossroads, his ambitions casting shadows on the path ahead. The slim figure that once roamed the sun-soaked beaches of St. Kitts has transformed into a figure of calculated intent. His eyes, once filled with youthful naivety, have hardened with the weight of his choices.

Ambition fuels his every move—a burning desire to climb the cartel's hierarchical ladder. Loyalties are tested as alliances shift like sand beneath his feet. Joseph understands that pursuing power demands a delicate dance, where one misstep could lead to irreparable consequences.

Yet, amidst the intrigue and danger, the spectre of his past haunts Joseph. The memories of the sunlit beaches and the laughter of childhood friends echo in the recesses of his mind, a reminder of the life he left behind. As he navigates the murky waters of criminal enterprises, he grapples with the cost of his ambitions and the toll it takes on the fragments of morality that still linger within.

Joseph's story unfolds at the crossroads of loyalty, ambition, morality, and survival. As he traverses the clandestine corridors of the Acosta cartel, he is faced with decisions that will define the man he becomes. The sunsets over St. Kitts, once a tranquil backdrop to his childhood, now mark the end of each day in a world where shadows reign, and the price of ambition is paid in increments of one's soul.

Character Description: Charline Bate

Name: Charline Bate
   Nationality: Australian
   Age: 36
   Height: 5 feet 4 inches
   Build: Slim
   Eyes: Blue
   Residence: From Australia, now living in St Kitts.

Backstory

Amidst the lush landscapes of St. Kitts, where the Caribbean breeze carries whispers of tranquillity and trepidation, Chaline Bate carved her unconventional path. This journey began far away in the sunburnt terrains of Australia. A woman of unwavering conviction, Chaline chose a life that defied norms, stepping into the shadows of the family business—arms dealing.

Chaline's story started in the sprawling vistas of Australia, where the harsh sun painted the landscapes with hues of red and gold. Born into a family whose roots ran deep into the rugged terrains of the Outback, Chaline inherited a legacy that resonated with strength and defiance. Her family, with a history entwined with firearms and the art of weaponry, were renowned for their skills and unorthodox trade.

From a young age, Chaline exhibited a sharp intellect and an innate understanding of the intricate world her family navigated. The echoes of gunshots and the scent of gunpowder became as familiar to her as the arid winds that swept across the Australian plains. The family business, though unconventional, was a source of pride, and Chaline absorbed its complexities with an almost intuitive grasp.

As the years unfolded, Chaline's resolve to follow in her family's footsteps solidified. She embraced the art of arms dealing, honing her skills with weapons of every kind. From the intricate mechanics of firearms to the subtle nuances of negotiation, Chaline's education went beyond the conventional boundaries, and her apprenticeship in the family business was an unspoken rite of passage.

Her family's reputation as arms dealers transcended borders, establishing a network that reached far beyond the Australian horizon. Chaline became an integral part of this intricate web, her involvement extending to dealings with clients whose motivations ranged from national defence to covert operations. Her keen business acumen and unyielding commitment to discretion garnered respect in the clandestine circles she navigated.

In pursuit of new opportunities and perhaps an escape from the arid landscapes of her homeland, Chaline found herself drawn to the vibrant allure of St. Kitts. The azure seas and the tropical embrace offered a stark contrast to the Australian terrains, and it was here, amidst the kaleidoscope of colours, that Chaline set up her operations.

St. Kitts, a haven that concealed both beauty and intrigue, became the backdrop for Chaline's unorthodox career. Her business, now international in scope, thrived in the shadows cast by the swaying palms and crystalline waters. Arms dealing became an art form, and Chaline, the master orchestrator, conducted her transactions with a blend of grace and ruthlessness.

In the cutthroat world of arms dealing, where loyalties are fragile and alliances ever-shifting, Chaline Bate held a steadfast principle—she would not peddle her wares to those connected with terrorism. While her family's legacy was built on the trade of lethal instruments, Chaline drew a moral line in the sand. Her weapons would not find their way into the hands of those who sought to sow chaos and destruction under the guise of political or ideological motives.

This principled stance brought challenges and adversaries, but Chaline remained unyielding. Her refusal to compromise on matters of terrorism elevated her reputation in certain circles, earning her both respect and enemies. The underbelly of arms dealing is a realm where ethics are often sacrificed for profit. Still, Chaline's unwavering commitment to her principles set her apart in a world where shadows danced with danger.

In the heart of St. Kitts, where the tropical sun painted the skies with hues of orange and pink, Chaline Bate operated from the shadows. Her life was a tapestry woven with secrecy, negotiation, and a steadfast commitment to a unique moral code. While her family's legacy cast a long shadow over her journey, Chaline navigated the intricate world of arms, dealing with a grace that belied the cruelty inherent in her chosen profession.

Character Description: Gary Jones

Name: Gary Jones
   Nationality: English
   Age: 45
   Height: 5 feet 7 inches
   Build: Stocky
   Eyes: Blue
   Residence: Isle Of Wight

Backstory

Amidst the quaint coastal charm of Shanklin, nestled on the picturesque Isle of Wight, Gary Jones found solace and purpose after a tumultuous journey that began amidst the rigours of military life. Born into a family with a long tradition of service to the British Armed Forces, Gary's destiny seemed etched in the discipline and honour that defined his lineage.

Gary felt the call to serve his country from a young age, inspired by tales of courage and sacrifice passed down through generations. Straight out of school, he enlisted in the esteemed Royal Marines, embarking on a journey that would shape his life. The rigorous training, the camaraderie forged in the crucible of hardship, and the unwavering commitment to duty became the cornerstones of his character.

As a Royal Marine, Gary thrived in the demanding environment, excelling in combat training, marksmanship, and leadership. His dedication and proficiency earned him the respect of his peers and superiors alike, propelling him through the ranks with a quiet determination that spoke volumes of his unwavering resolve.

Gary's service took him to the far corners of the globe, from the deserts of the Middle East to the dense jungles of Southeast Asia. He faced the trials of combat with stoicism, his courage unwavering even in the face of unimaginable danger. Yet, amidst the adrenaline-fueled chaos of warfare, Gary witnessed the harsh realities of conflict—the toll it took on the human spirit, the sacrifices demanded of those who served, and the scars that lingered long after the battles had ceased.

Throughout his deployments, Gary distinguished himself with acts of bravery and selflessness, earning commendations for his valour under fire. But with each medal pinned to his chest came the weight of loss—the comrades fallen in the line of duty, the civilians caught in the crossfire, and the toll it took on his own psyche. Amidst the chaos of war, Gary found solace in the bonds forged with his fellow Marines, drawing strength from their shared sense of purpose and camaraderie.

After years of service marked by sacrifice, Gary made the difficult decision to transition to civilian life. Returning to the idyllic shores of Shanklin, he sought refuge in the familiar embrace of his hometown, hoping to leave behind the echoes of warfare that haunted his dreams. Taking up a humble job as a barman at the local pub, The Barleycorn, Gary found solace in the routine of everyday life. The comforting rhythm of pouring pints and sharing banter with patrons was a balm for his weary soul.

Despite his desire for a quiet existence, Gary's past would soon catch up with him unexpectedly. Drawn into the orbit of Steve and his team, a group of individuals embroiled in a world of intrigue and danger, Gary found himself once again called upon to serve. His keen instincts honed in the crucible of combat proved invaluable in navigating the murky waters of espionage and subterfuge, his unwavering loyalty to his comrades driving him to lend his skills to their cause time and time again.

As Gary navigates the complexities of his newfound role as a civilian and a trusted ally to Steve and his team, he confronts the ghosts of his past with courage and resilience. With each challenge he faces and each life he touches, Gary Jones continues to embody the values of honour, duty, and sacrifice that define his journey from Royal Marine.

Character Description: Desmond Adolphine

Name: Desmond Adolphine
  Nationality: Kittian
  Age: 50
  Height: 5 feet 7 inches
  Build: slim
  Eyes: Brown
  Residence: St Kitts

Backstory

In the heart of the Caribbean, amidst the gentle sway of palm trees and the rhythmic lapping of waves against the shore, resides Desmond Adolphine—a weathered fisherman whose life is entwined with the ebb and flow of the ocean's currents. With his rough hands and sun-worn face, Desmond is a testament to the resilience of those who make their living on the sea.

Desmond's story begins in a quaint fishing village nestled along the island's shores. There, he spent his childhood surrounded by the salt-kissed air and the call of seabirds overhead. From a young age, Desmond was drawn to the vast expanse of the ocean, finding solace and purpose amidst its boundless depths.

Under the guidance of his father, a seasoned fisherman renowned for his skill and wisdom, Desmond learned the ancient art of navigating the treacherous waters surrounding their island home. With each sunrise, father and son would set out to sea aboard the "Marlin," their trusty vessel, casting their nets and lines with a practised hand.

Desmond's bond with the ocean deepened as the years passed, becoming an inseparable part of his identity. His fishing expeditions became more than just a means of livelihood; they were a sacred communion with the natural world, a dance of life and death played out on the shimmering surface of the sea.

Despite the inherent dangers of his profession, Desmond approached each day with a quiet resolve, guided by his father's lessons and the timeless wisdom of the ocean itself. His encounters with fierce storms and elusive catches only strengthened his connection to the sea, forging him into a seasoned mariner with an innate understanding of its moods and mysteries.

Beneath his weathered exterior, Desmond possesses a kind heart and a deep reverence for life in all its forms. He is known among his fellow fishermen as a steadfast friend and a compassionate listener, always willing to lend a helping hand or offer encouragement to those in need.

Desmond's love for the ocean extends beyond mere livelihood; a profound spiritual connection shapes his worldview and informs his interactions with the world around him. He treats each creature he encounters with respect and dignity, recognising the delicate balance that sustains life both above and below the waves.

As Desmond's boat cuts through the azure waters, he remains a silent sentinel, vigilant in his watch over the ocean he holds dear. His years of experience have made him a skilled navigator and a shrewd judge of character, allowing him to navigate the treacherous currents of both sea and society easily.

At the heart of it all, Desmond is a guardian of the seas—a protector of life's abundance and a steward of its fragile ecosystems. His unwavering commitment to his craft and community serves as a beacon of hope and resilience in a world shaped by the ebb and flow of the tides.

One fateful day, as Desmond tends to his nets near the pier, he crosses paths with Steve and the team, drawn together by a shared sense of purpose and a mutual respect for the ocean's bounty. Their encounter at the Dieppe Bay Cafe on the Pier marks the beginning of a journey fraught with danger and discovery, as Desmond's intimate knowledge of the sea becomes a vital asset in their quest for justice and redemption.

Character Description: Leroy "El Labo" Cuffy

Name: Leroy Cuffy:
  Nationality: Kittian
  Age: 36
  Height: 5 feet 9 inches
  Build: Muscular
  Eyes: Brown
  Residence: Oranjestad

Backstory.

In the shadowy underworld of organised crime, Leroy 'El Labo' Cuffy was a name whispered in hushed tones—a figure shrouded in darkness, feared and revered in equal measure. With a past steeped in violence and a reputation forged in blood, Leroy had clawed his way to the upper echelons of the Alex Acosta Cartel, carving out a niche for himself as one of its most ruthless enforcers.

Leroy's story began in the sprawling streets of Oranjestad, where he was raised amidst the poverty and desperation that plagued the island. Born into a family with deep ties to the criminal underworld, Leroy's fate seemed predestined from the moment he took his first breath. His father, a notorious enforcer for the Acosta Cartel, instilled in him the values of loyalty, obedience, and, above all, survival.

From a young age, Leroy was groomed for a life of crime, his childhood innocence stripped away by the harsh realities of his environment. He learned the art of violence at his father's knee, honing his skills in combat and intimidation with a cold, methodical precision that belied his tender years.

As Leroy came of age, he quickly made a name for himself within the ranks of the Cartel, earning the moniker 'El Labo'—the

Hammer—a testament to his brutal efficiency and unwavering commitment to the cause. With each passing year, he climbed the ladder of power, leaving a trail of broken bodies and shattered lives in his wake.

His reputation as a ruthless enforcer preceded him, striking fear into the hearts of both rivals and allies alike. Leroy's loyalty to the Cartel was unwavering, and his allegiance to Alex Acosta was absolute. He was a force to be reckoned with, a living embodiment of the Cartel's iron-fisted rule.

But beneath the veneer of power and prestige, Leroy bore the scars of a life steeped in darkness and the years of violence and bloodshed had taken their toll on his psyche, weighing heavily on his conscience and eroding whatever semblance of humanity remained within him. The faces of those he had harmed haunted his dreams, their silent accusations a constant reminder of the atrocities he had committed in the name of loyalty.

As the body count mounted and the Cartel's grip on the island tightened, Leroy became increasingly disillusioned with his chosen path. The lines between right and wrong blurred, and the spectre of his own mortality loomed large on the horizon. Deep down, he yearned for redemption—a chance to break free from the shackles of his past and forge a new path forward.

One fateful day, as Leroy patrolled the streets of Oranjestad, he crossed paths with Steve and the team—a chance encounter that would alter the course of his life forever. Drawn to their unwavering sense of justice and refusal to bow to the Cartel's tyranny, Leroy saw a glimmer of hope in them—a chance at redemption he had long thought beyond his grasp.

A meeting at a dingy bar on the outskirts of town marked the beginning of Leroy's transformation—a journey fraught with danger and uncertainty but also with the promise of redemption. As he joined forces with Steve and the team, he found himself torn between the bonds of loyalty that bound him to the Cartel and the newfound sense of purpose that pulsed within him like a beacon of light in the darkness.

Ultimately, Leroy would have to confront his demons head-on, face the consequences of his past actions, and choose between loyalty and redemption. But one thing was sure—whatever path he chose, Leroy 'El Labo' Cuffy would leave an indelible mark on the fate of Oranjestad and the lives of those who called it home.

STEPHEN BARKER

Locations, Cafés, Bars and Transport

Locations

Shanklin

Shanklin, nestled on the picturesque Isle of Wight off the southern coast of England, exudes timeless charm and natural beauty. This quaint coastal town is renowned for its stunning beaches, rugged cliffs, and lush greenery, making it a haven for nature lovers and holidaymakers.

One of Shanklin's most iconic features is its golden sandy beach, flanked by towering cliffs that provide a dramatic backdrop to the shimmering waters of the English Channel. Shanklin Beach offers something for everyone, whether looking to soak up the sun, stroll along the shore, or indulge in thrilling water sports.

In addition to its natural attractions, Shanklin boasts a vibrant town centre brimming with character. Here, you'll find an array of charming cafes, boutique shops, and traditional pubs where you can sample delicious local cuisine and mingle with friendly locals.

For those with a penchant for history, Shanklin offers glimpses into its storied past through landmarks such as Shanklin Chine, a lush ravine adorned with cascading waterfalls and exotic flora. Stroll through this enchanting gorge and uncover centuries of natural and human history.

Adventure seekers will find plenty to explore in Shanklin's surrounding countryside, with scenic walking trails, cycling routes, and hidden coves waiting to be discovered. Whether you're embarking on a coastal hike along the Isle of Wight Coastal Path or exploring the tranquil woodlands of Shanklin Down, the opportunities for outdoor adventure are endless.

At the end of a day of exploration, unwind in one of Shanklin's charming accommodations, ranging from cosy bed and breakfasts to luxury seaside hotels. With its captivating beauty and warm hospitality, Shanklin invites visitors to experience the best coastal living on the Isle of Wight.

Southampton

Southampton, a bustling port city on the south coast of England, is a vibrant blend of history, culture, and maritime charm. Situated at the confluence of the rivers Test and Itchen, Southampton has been a pivotal center of trade and commerce for centuries, with a rich maritime heritage that continues to shape its identity today.

At the heart of Southampton lies its historic Old Town, where medieval walls stand as a testament to its ancient past. Cobbled streets wind their way past timber-framed buildings and hidden alleys, offering a glimpse into the city's storied history. Visitors can explore attractions such as the Tudor House and Garden, a meticulously restored 15th-century dwelling that provides a fascinating insight into life in medieval Southampton.

For maritime enthusiasts, Southampton's connection to the sea is palpable. The city's bustling docks are home to one of the world's largest and busiest cruise ports, welcoming thousands of passengers each year to embark on voyages to destinations far and wide. The SeaCity Museum pays homage to Southampton's maritime legacy with interactive exhibits that delve into the city's role in the Titanic tragedy and its broader maritime history.

Beyond its maritime allure, Southampton offers a dynamic cultural scene with a thriving arts and music scene, vibrant nightlife, and an eclectic dining scene. From contemporary art galleries and theatres to live music venues and trendy bars, there's no shortage of entertainment options to suit every taste.

Nature lovers will also find plenty to explore in Southampton's green spaces, including the sprawling Southampton Common, a verdant oasis in the city's heart that offers miles of walking trails, sports facilities, and tranquil lakeside vistas.

With its fascinating history, vibrant culture, and scenic waterfront, Southampton invites visitors to embark on a journey of discovery and exploration along England's enchanting south coast.

Marlands Shopping Centre Southampton

Marlands Shopping Centre, nestled in the heart of Southampton's bustling city centre, is a vibrant retail destination that offers a diverse shopping experience for visitors of all ages. With its convenient location and eclectic mix of stores, Marlands is a popular destination for locals and tourists alike.

Step inside Marlands and immerse yourself in a world of fashion, beauty, and lifestyle. The centre is home to many shops, from high-street favourites to boutique retailers, offering everything from the latest fashion trends to unique gifts and accessories.

Fashionistas will delight in exploring the array of clothing stores, where they can browse racks of stylish apparel, footwear, and accessories from well-known brands and independent designers. Whether you are searching for the perfect outfit for a special occasion or simply updating your wardrobe with the latest trends, Marlands has something to suit every style and budget.

In addition to fashion, Marlands also boasts a diverse selection of beauty and cosmetics stores, where shoppers can stock up on skincare essentials, makeup must-haves, and fragrances from leading brands. Whether treating yourself to a pampering session or searching for the perfect gift, you'll find plenty of options.

Beyond fashion and beauty, Marlands offers a range of other amenities and services to enhance your shopping experience. Grab a bite to eat at one of the centre's cafes or restaurants, refuel with a coffee, or indulge in a delicious meal before continuing your shopping spree. With convenient parking facilities and easy access to public transport, getting to and from Marlands is a breeze.

Whether hunting for the latest fashion trends, searching for the perfect gift, or simply enjoying a leisurely shopping day, Marlands Shopping Centre offers everything you need for a memorable retail experience in the heart of Southampton.

West Quay Shopping Centre Food Court Southampton

The Westquay Shopping Centre Food Court in Southampton is a culinary haven for shoppers seeking a delicious break from their retail adventures. Nestled within the bustling Westquay complex, this vibrant food court offers diverse dining options to suit every taste and craving.

Step into the food court, and you'll find yourself surrounded by a tantalising mix of aromas and flavours from around the world. From fast-casual eateries to international cuisine, there's something to satisfy every palate.

For those craving a taste of the Mediterranean, there are Italian trattorias serving up piping hot pizzas and hearty pasta dishes and Greek eateries offering mouthwatering souvlaki and mezze platters.

Asian food enthusiasts can choose from various options, including sushi bars, noodle houses, and Thai restaurants, where they can sample authentic flavours and exotic spices in every bite.

Fans of American cuisine will find plenty to love in the food court, with burger joints, barbecue pits, and Tex-Mex diners serving up juicy burgers, succulent ribs, and loaded nachos.

Health-conscious diners are also well catered to, with various eateries offering fresh salads, smoothie bowls, and plant-based options to fuel their shopping adventures.

And, of course, no visit to the food court would be complete without indulging in a sweet treat or two. From artisanal gelato and freshly baked pastries to decadent desserts and gourmet chocolates, there's plenty to satisfy your sweet tooth.

With its diverse culinary offerings, relaxed atmosphere, and convenient location within the Westquay Shopping Centre, the food court is the perfect place to refuel and recharge during your shopping spree in Southampton. Whether grabbing a quick bite on the go or settling in for a leisurely meal with friends and family, the Westquay Food Court offers something for everyone to enjoy.

Harbour Village Beach Club

Harbour Village Beach Club, nestled on the stunning island of Bonaire in the Dutch Caribbean, is a luxurious oceanfront resort that offers guests an unparalleled blend of natural beauty, relaxation, and adventure. Situated on a pristine stretch of white sandy beach overlooking the azure waters of the Caribbean Sea, this exclusive retreat is the epitome of tropical paradise.

Accommodations at Harbour Village Beach Club are elegantly appointed, with spacious suites and villas that blend Caribbean charm with modern amenities. Each accommodation boasts breathtaking views of the ocean or lush gardens, providing guests with a serene escape from the hustle and bustle of everyday life.

The resort's beachfront location offers guests direct access to some of the Caribbean's best diving and snorkelling sites, including the nearby Bonaire National Marine Park. Whether you're an experienced diver or a novice snorkeler, the crystal-clear waters of Bonaire beckon with vibrant coral reefs, colourful marine life, and underwater wonders waiting to be explored.

For those seeking relaxation, Harbour Village Beach Club offers a range of amenities to indulge the senses and soothe the soul. Lounge by the sparkling infinity pool, stroll along the powdery white sands of the private beach or unwind with a rejuvenating spa treatment at the on-site spa.

Dining at Harbour Village Beach Club is a culinary delight, with various gourmet restaurants and bars serving tantalising cuisine inspired by the flavours of the Caribbean and beyond. From fresh seafood and tropical cocktails to international specialities, there's something to satisfy every palate.

Harbour Village Beach Club invites guests to experience the ultimate Caribbean getaway with its idyllic setting, luxurious accommodations, and world-class amenities. Whether you're seeking adventure, relaxation, or simply a slice of paradise, this exclusive resort offers a truly unforgettable escape in the heart of Bonaire.

Basseterre, the vibrant capital city of St. Kitts and Nevis

Basseterre, the vibrant capital city of St. Kitts and Nevis, is a captivating blend of colonial charm, Caribbean culture, and modern amenities. Nestled along the island's scenic coastline, this historic port city serves as the federation's cultural, economic, and political hub, welcoming visitors with its colourful architecture, bustling markets, and warm island hospitality.

One of the first things that strike visitors to Basseterre is its charming colonial architecture, with quaint pastel-coloured buildings lining its cobblestone streets. The city's historic landmarks, such as Independence Square and the Berkeley Memorial Clock Tower, offer glimpses into its colonial past and provide a sense of its rich cultural heritage.

Basseterre is also a shopper's paradise, with bustling markets and boutique shops offering a treasure trove of local handicrafts, souvenirs, and Caribbean-inspired goods. Visitors can browse the stalls of the Basseterre Craft Market for unique gifts and souvenirs or explore the city's chic boutiques for stylish fashion and accessories.

Food lovers will delight in Basseterre's vibrant culinary scene, which showcases a fusion of Caribbean flavours with international influences. From street food vendors serving savoury snacks to fine dining restaurants offering gourmet cuisine, there's something to tantalise every palate in Basseterre.

For those interested in history and culture, Basseterre offers a wealth of attractions to explore. The National Museum of St. Kitts provides insights into the island's heritage, with exhibits showcasing artefacts, artworks, and historical documents. At the same time, the St. George's Anglican Church offers a glimpse into the island's religious traditions with its beautiful stained-glass windows and colonial-era architecture.

Nature lovers will also find plenty to enjoy in Basseterre. Nearby attractions such as the lush rainforests of the central highlands and the scenic beaches of Frigate Bay offer hiking, birdwatching, and water sports opportunities.

With its captivating blend of history, culture, and natural beauty, Basseterre invites visitors to immerse themselves in the vibrant spirit of St. Kitts and Nevis and discover the magic of the Caribbean's hidden gem. Whether you're strolling along its historic streets, sampling its culinary delights, or soaking up the sun on its pristine beaches, Basseterre offers an unforgettable experience that captures the essence of island life.

St Kitts Cruise Port

The St. Kitts Cruise Port, located in Basseterre, the capital city of St. Kitts and Nevis, is a bustling gateway to the rich culture, stunning landscapes, and warm hospitality of this enchanting Caribbean Island. Welcoming thousands of cruise ship passengers each year, the port serves as a vibrant hub of activity, offering visitors a diverse array of experiences and attractions to explore during their time ashore.

As cruise ships dock at the port, passengers are greeted by the breathtaking vistas of St. Kitts' lush green hills, pristine beaches, and azure waters. The port's convenient location in the heart of Basseterre provides travellers easy access to the city's historic landmarks, shopping districts, and cultural attractions, making it an ideal starting point for exploring the island.

One of the highlights of a visit to the St. Kitts Cruise Port is the bustling waterfront area, where visitors can stroll along the promenade, browse local handicrafts at the souvenir shops, or sample traditional Caribbean cuisine at the waterfront cafes and restaurants. The port's lively atmosphere offers a taste of the island's vibrant culture and warm hospitality, inviting travellers to immerse themselves in the local way of life.

For those seeking adventure, the St. Kitts Cruise Port offers a variety of shore excursions and activities to suit every interest. From zip-lining through the rainforest and snorkelling along vibrant coral reefs to exploring historic plantations and hiking to scenic viewpoints, there's something for everyone to enjoy during their time ashore.

In addition to its recreational offerings, the St. Kitts Cruise Port also provides essential services and amenities for cruise ship passengers, including information desks, restrooms, and shuttle services to transport visitors between the port and downtown Basseterre.

With its stunning scenery, rich cultural heritage, and wide range of activities and attractions, the St. Kitts Cruise Port offers travellers an unforgettable introduction to the beauty and charm of St. Kitts and Nevis. Whether exploring historic landmarks, soaking up the sun on the beach, or immersing yourself in the island's vibrant culture, the port provides a memorable Caribbean experience for cruise ship passengers of all ages.

St Kitts & Nevis Independence Square

Independence Square, located in the heart of Basseterre, the capital city of St. Kitts and Nevis, is a historic and cultural landmark that is the focal point of the island's national identity. Originally known as Pall Mall Square during the colonial era, Independence Square holds great significance as the site where St. Kitts and Nevis was granted independence from British colonial rule on September 19, 1983.

The square is a vibrant hub of activity, bustling with locals and visitors alike and surrounded by some of Basseterre's most iconic landmarks. At its centre stands the Berkeley Memorial Clock Tower, a historical monument erected in honour of Thomas Berkeley, a former president of the St. Kitts-Nevis-Anguilla National Bank. The clock tower stands tall amidst the capital's bustling streets, symbolising the island's resilience and progress.

Surrounding Independence Square are rows of colourful colonial-style buildings, many of which now house government offices, businesses, and shops. The architecture reflects the island's rich colonial heritage, with ornate facades and balconies adding to the square's historic charm.

Independence Square is a place of historical significance and a gathering place for cultural events, celebrations, and festivals throughout the year. From Independence Day parades and cultural performances to food festivals and art exhibitions, the square comes alive with the vibrant energy and spirit of the island's people.

Visitors to Independence Square can take a leisurely stroll around the manicured gardens, relax on benches beneath the shade of towering palm trees, or soak up the atmosphere of this iconic landmark. Whether you're interested in history and culture or simply enjoying the beauty of Basseterre, Independence Square offers a memorable experience that captures the essence of St. Kitts and Nevis' proud heritage.

Canda Hill Estate on St Kitts

Cane Hill Estate, nestled in the lush countryside of St. Kitts, is a historic plantation that offers visitors a fascinating glimpse into the island's colonial past and rich agricultural heritage. Situated on the slopes of Mount Liamuiga, the estate's verdant fields, historic buildings, and panoramic views make it a must-visit destination for history buffs and nature lovers alike.

Initially established in the 17th century, Cane Hill Estate played a central role in St. Kitts' sugar industry, which flourished during the island's colonial period. The estate's sprawling fields were once home to vast sugar cane plantations worked by enslaved African labourers.

Today, Cane Hill Estate is a living testament to St. Kitts' complex history. Visitors can explore the estate's beautifully restored Great House, a grand colonial-era mansion that offers insights into the lives of the island's plantation owners and their families. The Great House is filled with period furnishings, artefacts, and exhibits that tell the story of the estate's past, from its days as a sugar plantation to its more recent history as a working farm.

In addition to the Great House, Cane Hill Estate boasts acres of picturesque grounds to explore, including lush gardens, tropical orchards, and scenic walking trails. Visitors can take leisurely walks through the estate's manicured gardens, admiring the vibrant flowers and exotic plants that thrive in St. Kitts' tropical climate.

For those interested in learning more about the island's agricultural heritage, Cane Hill Estate offers guided tours that provide insights into the cultivation of sugar cane, cocoa, and other crops grown on the estate. Visitors can learn about traditional farming techniques, sample fresh produce grown on the estate, and even participate in hands-on activities such as cocoa bean harvesting or sugar cane pressing.

With its rich history, stunning natural beauty, and immersive visitor experiences, Cane Hill Estate offers a captivating journey through St. Kitts's past and present. Whether you're exploring the estate's historic buildings, strolling through its scenic gardens, or learning about its agricultural traditions, a visit to Cane Hill Estate will surely be a memorable experience for all who visit.

Dieppe Bay Town St Kitts

Dieppe Bay Town, nestled on the northern coast of St. Kitts in the Caribbean, is a charming seaside village renowned for its picturesque landscapes, rich history, and laid-back island vibes. Named after the French port city of Dieppe, which shares historical ties, this quaint town offers visitors a glimpse into the authentic Caribbean way of life.

One of Dieppe Bay Town's defining features is its stunning natural beauty. The town is surrounded by lush green hills, swaying palm trees, and pristine beaches lapped by the turquoise waters of the Caribbean Sea. The rugged coastline and dramatic cliffs provide a dramatic backdrop for leisurely walks along the shore or breathtaking sunset views.

Dieppe Bay Town is also steeped in history, with traces of its colonial past still visible in its architecture and landmarks. Visitors can explore historical sites such as the Dieppe Bay Petroglyphs and ancient rock carvings believed to be the work of indigenous peoples, offering insights into the island's pre-Columbian history.

For outdoor enthusiasts, Dieppe Bay Town offers a wealth of recreational activities. From snorkelling and diving in the crystal-clear waters of the nearby reef to hiking through the lush rainforests of the surrounding hills, there's no shortage of adventure to be had in this picturesque corner of St. Kitts.

Despite its small size, Dieppe Bay Town is home to a vibrant community with a rich cultural heritage. Visitors can immerse themselves in the local culture by attending traditional festivals, sampling authentic Caribbean cuisine, or simply chatting with friendly locals at one of the town's charming cafes or beachside bars.

With its breathtaking scenery, fascinating history, and warm island hospitality, Dieppe Bay Town invites visitors to experience the beauty and charm of St. Kitts' northern coast. Whether you're seeking relaxation, adventure, or a glimpse into the island's cultural heritage, this hidden gem offers a truly unforgettable Caribbean experience.

Brimstone Hill Fort St Kitts

Brimstone Hill Fortress National Park, perched majestically atop a volcanic peak on the island of St. Kitts in the Caribbean, is a UNESCO World Heritage Site and a testament to the island's rich history and strategic importance. Often referred to as the "Gibraltar of the Caribbean," this formidable fortress offers visitors a glimpse into the island's colonial past and provides breathtaking panoramic views of the surrounding landscapes and the Caribbean Sea.

Constructed over more than a century by African slave labour and European artisans, Brimstone Hill Fortress is a marvel of engineering and military architecture. Its massive stone walls and imposing bastions stand as a testament to the skill and ingenuity of its builders and the site's strategic significance in protecting the island from potential invaders.

Visitors to Brimstone Hill Fortress can explore the well-preserved ruins, including the barracks, gun emplacements, and officer's quarters, which offer insights into the daily life of soldiers stationed at the fort centuries ago. The on-site museum provides further context, with exhibits detailing the fortress's history and its role in the colonial conflicts of the Caribbean.

One of the highlights of a visit to Brimstone Hill Fortress is the breathtaking views from its elevated vantage point. From the top of the fortress, visitors can enjoy panoramic vistas of the surrounding countryside, with lush tropical forests, sugar cane fields, and distant islands stretching out to the horizon.

In addition to its historical and cultural significance, Brimstone Hill Fortress National Park is also home to a diverse array of plant and animal species, making it a haven for nature lovers and birdwatchers. Visitors can explore the park's hiking trails and discover the rich biodiversity of the Caribbean, including native birds, reptiles, and tropical flora.

With its stunning vistas, rich history, and natural beauty, Brimstone Hill Fortress offers visitors a truly unforgettable experience and a deeper understanding of St. Kitts' fascinating heritage. Whether you're a history buff, nature enthusiast, or simply seeking breathtaking views, a visit to Brimstone Hill Fortress will leave a lasting impression.

Oranjestad Island, Caribbean Netherlands

Oranjestad, located on the picturesque island of Sint Eustatius (Statia) in the Caribbean Netherlands, is a quaint and historic town that offers visitors a glimpse into the island's rich cultural heritage and natural beauty. Nestled on the western coast of Statia, Oranjestad serves as the capital and main port of this charming Dutch Caribbean Island.

Despite its small size, Oranjestad boasts a wealth of historic landmarks and architectural treasures that reflect its colonial past. Visitors can explore the town's cobblestone streets and narrow alleyways, admiring the well-preserved Dutch colonial buildings that date back to the 18th century. Highlights include the historic Fort Oranje, a stone fortress overlooking the harbour, and the Old Government House, which now serves as a museum showcasing the island's history and culture.

One of Oranjestad's defining features is its picturesque waterfront, where colourful boats bob in the harbour and palm trees sway in the gentle breeze. Visitors can stroll along the waterfront promenade, viewing the Caribbean Sea and neighbouring islands, or relax at one of the waterfront cafes and restaurants, savouring fresh seafood and local specialities.

Oranjestad is also home to a vibrant local community with a rich cultural heritage celebrated through festivals, music, and cuisine. Visitors can immerse themselves in the island's culture by attending traditional events such as the Statia Carnival or sampling authentic Caribbean dishes at local eateries and street food stalls.

Nature lovers will also find plenty to explore in and around Oranjestad, with hiking trails leading to scenic viewpoints, lush rainforests, and secluded beaches. Nearby attractions such as the Quill

National Park, a dormant volcano with hiking trails and diverse flora and fauna, offer outdoor adventure and wildlife spotting opportunities.

With its historic charm, stunning scenery, and warm island hospitality, Oranjestad invites visitors to experience the beauty and tranquillity of Sint Eustatius. Whether exploring its historic landmarks, soaking up the sun on its beautiful beaches, or immersing yourself in the island's vibrant culture, Oranjestad offers an unforgettable Caribbean experience.

Café and Bars

Cafe Calypso

Welcome to Cafe Calypso, a charming seaside retreat nestled along the picturesque coastline. With its relaxed ambience and panoramic ocean views, Cafe Calypso offers a delightful escape for tourists seeking a taste of coastal paradise. Savour freshly brewed coffee and delectable pastries while soaking in the gentle sea breeze from our outdoor patio. Whether you're looking to start your day with a leisurely breakfast or unwind with a sunset cocktail, Cafe Calypso invites you to indulge in a memorable dining experience by the sea.

Island Breeze Café

Welcome to Island Breeze Cafe, where the tropical vibes meet culinary delights! Located on the vibrant waterfront of our island paradise, Island Breeze offers a taste of local flavours infused with international flair. Enjoy freshly caught seafood dishes, refreshing fruit smoothies, and decadent desserts while basking in the warm island sunshine on our outdoor terrace. With its laid-back atmosphere and stunning views of the azure waters, Island Breeze Cafe is the perfect spot to relax, recharge, and soak up the island's charm. Join us for a culinary journey that captures the essence of our tropical paradise!

Dieppe Bay Café

Welcome to Dieppe Bay Cafe, where Caribbean charm meets culinary excellence! Nestled on the picturesque shores of Dieppe Bay, our cafe offers a delightful blend of local and international cuisine with breathtaking ocean views. Indulge in freshly brewed coffee, homemade pastries, and sumptuous Caribbean-inspired dishes crafted from the finest locally sourced ingredients. Whether you are seeking a leisurely breakfast, a light lunch, or a romantic dinner by the sea, Dieppe Bay Cafe promises an unforgettable dining experience in paradise. Sit back, relax, and savour the flavours of the Caribbean as gentle sea breezes and the sound of crashing waves serenade your senses at Dieppe Bay Cafe.

The Barleycorn

Welcome to The Barleycorn, a beloved pub nestled in the heart of Shanklin on the picturesque Isle of Wight. Step inside this charming historic building and soak in the cosy atmosphere, where traditional wooden beams and roaring fireplaces create a welcoming ambience. With its friendly staff and extensive selection of locally brewed ales, fine wines, and spirits, The Barleycorn is the perfect spot to unwind after a day of exploring the island. Sit back and relax in the inviting lounge area, or head out to the sunny beer garden to enjoy a refreshing drink al fresco. Whether you're craving classic pub fare or gourmet dishes made with locally sourced ingredients, The Barleycorn's menu has something to satisfy every palate. Don't miss out on the live music nights and quiz evenings, where you can mingle with locals and fellow travellers alike. For an authentic taste of Isle of Wight hospitality, make sure to visit The Barleycorn during your stay in Shanklin.

Costa Coffee Southampton

Welcome to Costa Coffee Southampton, a vibrant and inviting café in the city's heart. Step inside and be greeted by the rich aroma of freshly brewed coffee and the warm ambience of modern décor. Take a seat and indulge in a wide selection of expertly crafted coffee beverages, from classic espressos to creamy lattes. Feeling peckish? Costa Coffee offers a tempting array of pastries, sandwiches, and sweet treats to satisfy any craving. Sit back, relax, and soak in the bustling atmosphere as you enjoy your favourite brew or grab a coffee and explore Southampton's sights and sounds. With friendly staff and a commitment to quality, Costa Coffee Southampton is the perfect spot to refuel and recharge during your visit to the city.

The Siren's Call

Welcome to The Siren's Call, a hidden gem nestled along the sun-kissed shores of St. Kitts. As you approach this seaside oasis, you'll be enchanted by the gentle melody of waves lapping against the shore and the salty breeze carrying the promise of adventure. Step inside and be transported to a world of tropical charm and laid-back luxury.

The Siren's Call boasts a vibrant and colourful atmosphere, with open-air seating offering panoramic views of the azure Caribbean Sea. Whether you choose to relax in the shade of a palm tree or bask in the warm sunshine on the sandy shores, you'll find yourself immersed in the beauty of island life.

Savour the flavours of the Caribbean with a menu inspired by local cuisine, featuring fresh seafood, tropical fruits, and exotic spices. Indulge in island favourites like jerk chicken, coconut shrimp, and conch fritters, all expertly prepared by our talented chefs. Wash it down with a refreshing rum punch or a fruity cocktail crafted with locally sourced ingredients. As the sun dips below the horizon, The Siren's Call transforms into a vibrant hotspot for live music and entertainment.

Dance the night away to the rhythms of reggae, soca, and calypso, or unwind with a cold drink and the company of friends. Whether you're seeking a romantic evening for two or a lively gathering with friends, The Siren's Call offers an unforgettable experience that captures the spirit of St. Kitts. So join us and let the magic of The Siren's Call wash over you during your visit to this Caribbean paradise.

Airports & Ferries

London Heathrow Airport

London Heathrow Airport, one of the world's busiest and most iconic international airports, is a bustling gateway to the United Kingdom and beyond. Situated to the west of London, Heathrow serves as a major hub for both domestic and international flights, connecting millions of passengers to destinations across the globe each year.

Spread across five terminals, Heathrow offers a seamless travel experience with a wide range of facilities and amenities to cater to travellers' needs. From state-of-the-art terminals to world-class shopping and dining options, Heathrow Airport strives to provide passengers with a comfortable and convenient journey from start to finish.

Upon arrival at Heathrow, travellers are greeted by a bustling array of shops, restaurants, and services, making it easy to pass the time before departure or during layovers. From luxury boutiques and high-street retailers to duty-free outlets offering tax-free shopping, there's something for everyone to explore.

Food lovers will delight in the diverse dining options available at Heathrow. A wide range of restaurants, cafes, and bars serve delicious cuisine from around the world. Whether you're in the mood for a quick bite or a leisurely meal, you'll find plenty of options to satisfy your cravings.

In addition to its shopping and dining offerings, Heathrow boasts a range of amenities to ensure a stress-free travel experience. From lounges and prayer rooms to children's play areas and pet facilities, the airport caters to the needs of travellers of all ages and interests.

For those in need of assistance, Heathrow's friendly staff are on hand to provide help and guidance, whether it's navigating the airport, arranging onward travel, or answering any questions you may have.

With its world-class facilities, convenient location, and unparalleled connectivity, London Heathrow Airport is more than just a travel hub – it's a destination in its own right, offering a glimpse into the vibrant and diverse culture of the United Kingdom. Whether you're arriving, departing, or simply passing through, Heathrow promises an unforgettable travel experience from the moment you set foot in its terminals.

Bonaire Flamingo International Airport

Bonaire International Airport, also known as Flamingo International Airport, serves as the primary gateway to the captivating island of Bonaire in the southern Caribbean. Situated just a few miles from the island's capital, Kralendijk, this modern airport provides travellers with convenient access to Bonaire's pristine beaches, vibrant coral reefs, and natural wonders.

Despite its relatively small size, Bonaire International Airport offers a range of amenities and services to ensure passengers a comfortable and hassle-free travel experience. The terminal features modern facilities, including check-in counters, baggage claim areas, and security checkpoints, all designed to streamline the departure and arrival process.

Upon arrival at Bonaire International Airport, travellers are greeted by the warm Caribbean breeze and breathtaking views of the island's turquoise waters and lush landscapes. The airport's open-air design lets visitors immediately immerse themselves in the tropical ambience, setting the tone for an unforgettable vacation experience.

In addition to its passenger services, Bonaire International Airport is equipped to handle a variety of aircraft, including commercial jets, private planes, and charter flights. The airport's runway and apron facilities are well-maintained and capable of accommodating aircraft of various sizes, making it a popular choice for both scheduled and charter flights to and from the island.

For travellers with some time to spare before departure, Bonaire International Airport offers a small selection of shops and eateries where visitors can grab a snack or souvenir before boarding their flight. From local handicrafts and Caribbean delicacies to travel essentials and duty-free goods, there's something for everyone to enjoy.

With its convenient location, modern facilities, and laid-back Caribbean charm, Bonaire International Airport serves as the perfect starting point for an unforgettable island adventure. Whether you're arriving to explore Bonaire's world-class diving sites, relax on its pristine beaches, or immerse yourself in its rich culture and history, the airport welcomes you with open arms to this tropical paradise.

St. Kitts' Robert L. Bradshaw International Airport

St. Kitts' Robert L. Bradshaw International Airport serves as the primary gateway to the enchanting twin-island federation of St. Kitts and Nevis, welcoming travellers from around the world to this idyllic Caribbean destination. Located just a short distance from the capital city of Basseterre, this modern airport provides visitors with convenient access to the natural beauty, rich history, and warm hospitality that define the islands of St. Kitts and Nevis.

Upon arrival at Robert L. Bradshaw International Airport, travellers are greeted by the vibrant colours and tropical ambience that characterise the Caribbean. The airport's welcoming atmosphere sets the tone for a memorable island getaway, inviting visitors to immerse themselves in the laid-back charm and natural splendour of St. Kitts and Nevis from the moment they touch down.

The terminal building at Robert L. Bradshaw International Airport is equipped with a range of passenger services and amenities to ensure a comfortable and stress-free travel experience. From check-in counters and baggage claim areas to customs and immigration facilities, the airport is well-equipped to handle the needs of travellers arriving and departing from the island.

In addition to its passenger services, Robert L. Bradshaw International Airport can accommodate various aircraft, including commercial jets, private planes, and charter flights. The airport's runway and apron facilities are maintained to international standards, making it a popular choice for both scheduled and charter flights to and from St. Kitts.

For travellers with some time to spare before departure, Robert L. Bradshaw International Airport offers a selection of shops, restaurants, and duty-free outlets where visitors can shop for souvenirs, enjoy a meal, or relax with a refreshing beverage. Whether you're craving Caribbean cuisine or the perfect gift to take home, the airport's amenities cater to various tastes and preferences.

With its convenient location, modern facilities, and warm island welcome, Robert L. Bradshaw International Airport serves as the perfect starting point for an unforgettable journey to St. Kitts and Nevis. Whether you're arriving to explore the island's lush rainforests, pristine beaches, or historic landmarks, the airport invites you to experience the beauty and charm of the Caribbean in true island style.

Oranjestad Island International Airport

Oranjestad International Airport, located on the picturesque island of Sint Eustatius (Statia) in the Caribbean Netherlands, is the primary gateway to this charming Dutch Caribbean island. Nestled on the eastern coast of Statia, the airport provides essential air transportation connections for visitors and residents alike, facilitating travel to and from the island.

Despite its modest size, Oranjestad International Airport offers modern facilities and services to ensure a smooth and efficient travel experience for passengers. The terminal building features check-in counters, baggage claim areas, and security checkpoints, providing essential amenities for travellers departing or arriving on the island.

Upon arrival at Oranjestad International Airport, visitors are greeted by the warm Caribbean breeze and stunning views of the island's lush landscapes and turquoise waters. The airport's location on the eastern coast of Statia offers travellers a scenic introduction to the natural beauty and tranquillity of the island, setting the tone for a memorable Caribbean getaway.

In addition to its passenger services, Oranjestad International Airport is equipped to handle a variety of aircraft, including commercial jets, private planes, and charter flights. The airport's runway and apron facilities are well-maintained and capable of accommodating aircraft of various sizes, ensuring that travellers have access to a range of air transportation options when visiting the island.

For travellers with some time to spare before departure, Oranjestad International Airport offers a small selection of amenities, including a cafe and souvenir shop. Visitors can grab snacks or pick up last-minute gifts before boarding their flight.

With its convenient location, modern facilities, and warm island hospitality, Oranjestad International Airport serves as the perfect starting point for an unforgettable journey to Sint Eustatius. Whether you're arriving to explore the island's historic landmarks, soak up the sun on its beautiful beaches, or immerse yourself in its vibrant culture, the airport welcomes you with open arms to this hidden gem in the Dutch Caribbean.

Red Funnel Ferries

Red Funnel Ferries, based in Southampton, is a renowned ferry company providing vital transportation links between the mainland of England and the beautiful Isle of Wight. With a rich history dating back to the mid-19th century, Red Funnel has become integral to the region's maritime heritage, offering reliable and efficient ferry services for passengers and vehicles alike.

The company operates a fleet of modern ferries that ply the waters of the Solent, connecting Southampton on the mainland with the towns of East Cowes and West Cowes on the Isle of Wight. Red Funnel's ferries offer a comfortable and convenient way to travel between the two destinations, with regular sailings throughout the day and night.

Red Funnel's ferries are equipped with various amenities to ensure a pleasant journey for passengers. Onboard facilities may include spacious lounges, cafes, bars, and outdoor deck areas where travellers can relax and enjoy the scenic views of the Solent as they sail between Southampton and the Isle of Wight.

In addition to its passenger services, Red Funnel also provides transportation for vehicles, making it easy for travellers to bring their cars, bicycles, or motorcycles to the Isle of Wight. The company offers convenient vehicle loading and unloading facilities and ample parking at its terminals in Southampton and Cowes.

Red Funnel is committed to providing safe and environmentally responsible ferry services. Its focus is on sustainability and reducing its carbon footprint. The company invests in modern, fuel-efficient vessels and implements eco-friendly practices to minimise its impact on the marine environment.

With its reliable service, modern fleet, and commitment to customer satisfaction, Red Funnel Ferries is the preferred choice for travellers seeking a seamless and enjoyable journey between

Southampton and the Isle of Wight. Whether commuting for work, planning a day trip, or embarking on a holiday adventure, Red Funnel offers a convenient and efficient way to travel across the Solent.

www.ingramcontent.com/pod-product-compliance
Ingram Content Group UK Ltd.
Pitfield, Milton Keynes, MK11 3LW, UK
UKHW021421210125
4213UKWH00032B/512

9 798224 435296